CW00349902

DISNEY HITS

ALMOST THERE THE PRINCESS AND THE FROG 4

BE OUR GUEST BEAUTY AND THE BEAST 6

BUNDLE OF JOY INSIDE OUT 3

DOWN TO EARTH WALL-E 8

A DREAM IS A WISH YOUR HEART MAKES CINDERELLA 10

FOR THE FIRST TIME IN FOREVER FROZEN 12

I JUST CAN'T WAIT TO BE KING THE LION KING 14

I SEE THE LIGHT TANGLED 20

I THOUGHT I LOST YOU BOLT 17

IMMORTALS BIG HERO 6 22

LAVA LAVA 26

LET IT GO FROZEN 24

ONCE UPON A DREAM MALEFICENT 32

PART OF YOUR WORLD THE LITTLE MERMAID 29

REFLECTION MULAN 34

SHUT UP AND DRIVE WRECK-IT RALPH 36

STRONG CINDERELLA 38

THAT'S HOW YOU KNOW ENCHANTED 41

TOUCH THE SKY BRAVE 44

WE BELONG TOGETHER TOY STORY 3 46

ORDER NO. HLE90004882
ISBN 978-1-78558-111-3
THIS BOOK © COPYRIGHT 2015 HAL LEONARD.

MUSIC ARRANGED BY FIONA BOLTON.
MUSIC PROCESSED BY PAUL EWERS MUSIC DESIGN.
EDITED BY JENNI NOREY.
PRINTED IN THE EU.

YOUR GUARANTEE OF QUALITY
AS PUBLISHERS, WE STRIVE TO PRODUCE EVERY BOOK TO THE HIGHEST
COMMERCIAL STANDARDS. THE MUSIC HAS BEEN FRESHLY ENGRAVED AND
THE BOOK HAS BEEN CAREFULLY DESIGNED TO MINIMISE AWKWARD PAGE
TURNS AND TO MAKE PLAYING FROM IT A REAL PLEASURE.
PARTICULAR CARE HAS BEEN GIVEN TO SPECIFYING ACID-FREE, NEUTRAL-
SIZED PAPER MADE FROM PULPS WHICH HAVE NOT BEEN ELEMENTAL
CHLORINE BLEACHED. THIS PULP IS FROM FARMED SUSTAINABLE FORESTS
AND WAS PRODUCED WITH SPECIAL REGARD FOR THE ENVIRONMENT.
THROUGHOUT, THE PRINTING AND BINDING HAVE BEEN PLANNED TO
ENSURE A STURDY, ATTRACTIVE PUBLICATION WHICH SHOULD GIVE YEARS
OF ENJOYMENT. IF YOUR COPY FAILS TO MEET OUR HIGH STANDARDS,
PLEASE INFORM US AND WE WILL GLADLY REPLACE IT.

Bundle Of Joy

Music by Michael Giacchino

The soundtrack to 2015's *Inside Out* was written by Michael Giacchino, who has composed the music for several other Disney/Pixar films, including *Up* and *Ratatouille*. The film follows the story of a young girl growing up, from the viewpoint of personifications of the emotions in her head: Joy, Fear, Anger, Disgust and Sadness. 'Bundle Of Joy' is a simple and effective piano-based piece that is featured early on in the film.

Hints & Tips: Play the left-hand quavers with a 'rocking' motion to keep them even and steady. This piece should be quiet throughout.

Almost There

Words & Music by Randy Newman

This uplifting song from Disney's 2009 film *The Princess And The Frog* was composed by long-term collaborator Randy Newman and performed solo by actress Anika Noni Rose. The song describes how Tiana is so close to reaching her dream of opening her own restaurant, and proved so successful that it was nominated for the Best Original Song Oscar, as well as being released in 41 different languages!

Hints & Tips: Be on the lookout for accidentals, as they crop up frequently throughout. This should be played with confidence so break it down and practise in sections.

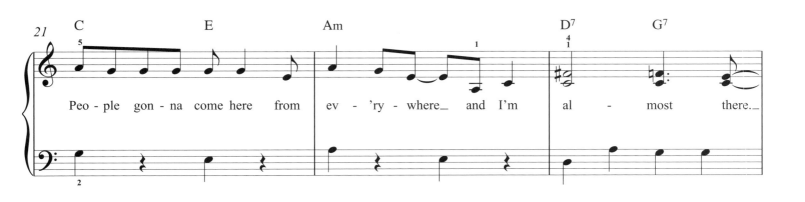

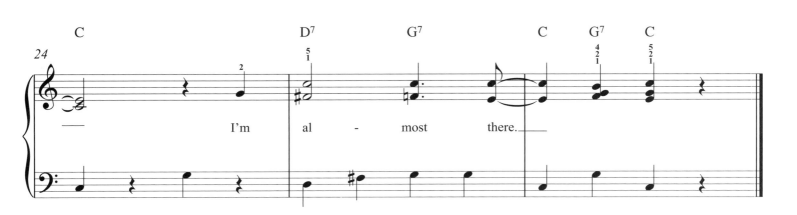

Be Our Guest

Words by Howard Ashman
Music by Alan Menken

Consistently rated by critics and Disney fans as one of the greatest songs from any Disney film, 'Be Our Guest' was originally sung by Jerry Orbach, as the singing candelabra Lumiere, and Angela Lansbury, as Mrs Potts. Composed by Alan Menken with lyrics by Howard Ashman, nearly every aspect of this true showstopper has been acclaimed, from the vocal performances and catchiness to the use of CGI during its sequence in the film.

Hints & Tips: Note the time signature; it means you need to count two minims per bar. Make sure you leave the full one-beat count for the crotchet rests in the left hand.

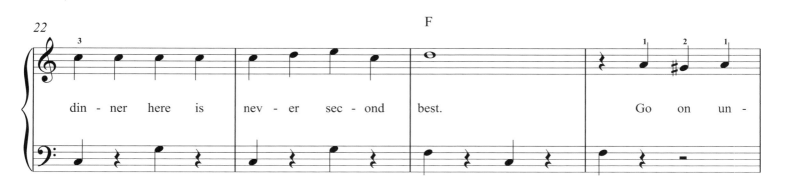

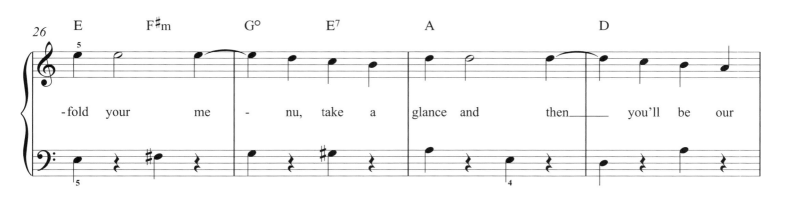

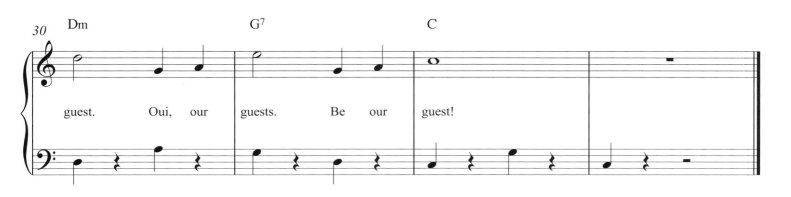

Down To Earth

Words by Peter Gabriel
Music by Peter Gabriel & Thomas Newman

Composer Thomas Newman and director Andrew Stanton enlisted singer and songwriter Peter Gabriel to perform the end-credits song for this blockbuster film about a waste-disposal robot. Gabriel is one of Stanton's favourite musicians, and Newman flew to London to compose this rousing anthem about environmental problems and our effect on the world – the principle themes of the film.

Hints & Tips: Start off softly at the beginning, so that there's a real contrast with the *forte* in bar 24. Note that the piece also changes key in the next bar.

9

A Dream Is A Wish Your Heart Makes

Words & Music by Mack David, Al Hoffman
& Jerry Livingston

This song was originally composed for the 1950 animated Disney film *Cinderella*, but this version was recorded by star Lily James for the 2015 live-action film's soundtrack. One of the most popular Disney songs, the tune features a wonderful melody as Cinderella optimistically sings of dreams coming true. Composed by Mack David, Al Hoffman and Jerry Livingston, the song was used over the end credits of Kenneth Branagh's film adaptation.

Hints & Tips: The melody is in the left hand throughout, so keep the right-hand chords soft to allow it to come through. Check the ledger lines from bar 25, working out the notes first and pencilling them in if you need to.

For The First Time In Forever

Words & Music by Robert Lopez & Kristen Anderson-Lopez

Boasting excellent vocals from Kristen Bell (Anna) and Idina Menzel (Elsa), 'For The First Time In Forever' tells the story of Anna's excitement when the gates are finally opened for Elsa's coronation. Elsa's part is a wonderful counterpoint melody that tells of her fear over accidentally revealing her powers. Filled with both seriousness and humour, the song features a line written by the writers' daughter: "I wanna stuff some chocolate in my face."

Hints & Tips: Play through any difficult-looking rhythms before you begin, making sure you count carefully. Look out for 2/4 bar towards the end.

I Just Can't Wait To Be King

Words by Tim Rice
Music by Elton John

One of five original songs written by Elton John and Tim Rice for the epic Disney classic *The Lion King*, 'I Just Can't Wait To Be King' is an upbeat number sung by a young Simba along with Nala, a young female lion, and Zazu, a hornbill who works for the king's household. During the song, Simba expresses his feelings about growing up and all the things he's looking forward to when he becomes king of Pride Rock and no longer has to be bossed around.

Hints & Tips: Don't let the tempo drag in this bright, optimistic song. The use of accidentals means the Bs are sometimes flat and sometimes natural; be careful you don't get caught out!

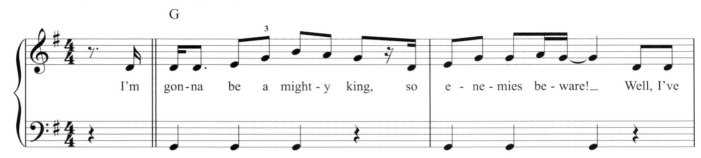

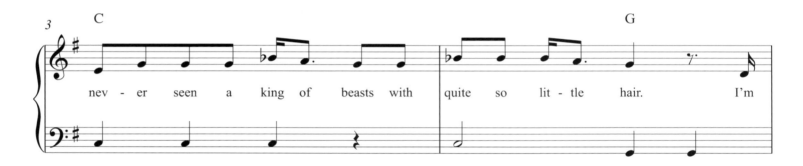

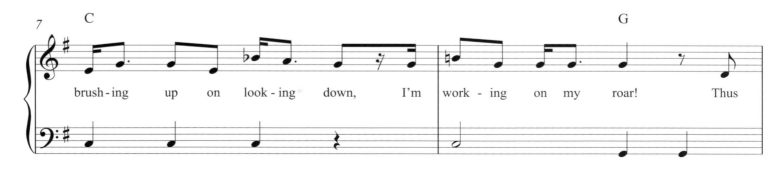

I Thought I Lost You

Words & Music by Jeffrey Steele & Miley Cyrus

Sung by Miley Cyrus and John Travolta for the 2008 film *Bolt*, Miley Cyrus wrote this after the filmmakers requested her to write and sing a song with her co-star John Travolta. Travolta, who voices the dog Bolt, agreed to sing the song even before it was written, and heavily praised Cyrus' song-writing talents when it was finished. The song was nominated for a Golden Globe Award for Best Original Song.

Hints & Tips: Make sure the notes of the left-hand chords sound together; use these steady crotchets to place the trickier right-hand rhythms.

Like some - how you could be_____ re - placed.

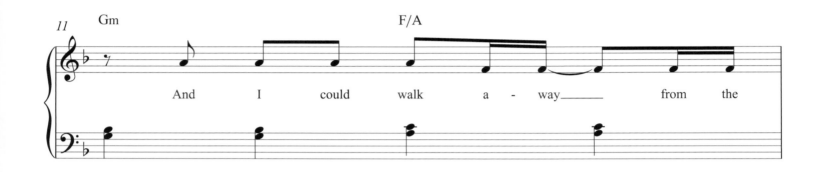

And I could walk a - way_____ from the

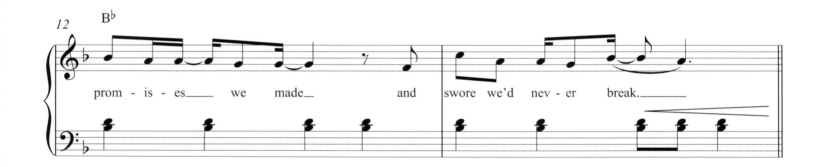

prom - is - es___ we made___ and swore we'd nev - er break._____

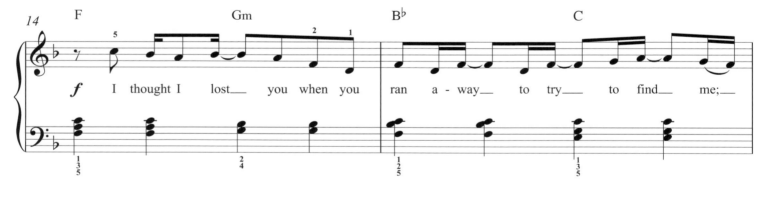

f I thought I lost__ you when you ran a - way__ to try__ to find__ me;__

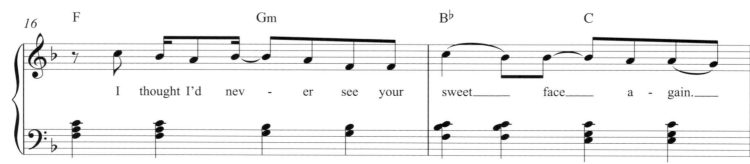

I thought I'd nev - er see your sweet___ face___ a - gain.___

I See The Light

Words by Glenn Slater
Music by Alan Menken

This song was composed by Alan Menken with lyrics by Glenn Slater for Disney's 50th animated film *Tangled*. Performed by Mandy Moore and Zachary Levi, who played Rapunzel and Flynn Rider respectively, the ballad accompanies the 'lantern scene' in the film, which was widely acclaimed by critics for the beauty of its animation. The sequence (and its 45,000 floating lanterns!) has been remembered for being the emotional peak of the film.

Hints & Tips: There are quite a few changes in position for the right hand, so check the fingering carefully. Play through bars 28 and 29 on their own till you can play the quavers smoothly.

Immortals

**Words & Music by Peter Wentz, Andrew Hurley,
Joseph Trohman & Patrick Stump**

When rock band Fall Out Boy were approached to write a song for the soundtrack of 2014's *Big Hero 6*, they immediately understood the meaning of the film and wrote 'Immortals'. According to bassist Pete Wentz, the idea of the characters coming together to achieve something great was something the band liked, stating that they always identified with the underdog. The song plays over the end credits of the film.

Hints & Tips: There are lots of quavers and semiquavers to get your fingers round in this fast-paced song, but try to keep the movement going.

Let It Go

Music and lyrics by Kirsten Anderson-Lopez and Robert Lopez

'Let It Go', first heard in Disney's hit 2013 film *Frozen*, has since become one of the best-selling singles of all time. Composed by husband and wife songwriters Kristen Anderson-Lopez and Robert Lopez, the song was written for and originally performed by Idina Menzel, whose powerful vocals perfectly voiced Elsa's newfound freedom in the film. The song was reportedly composed in just a single day, after an inspiring walk in New York's Prospect Park.

Hints & Tips: There's a lot to watch out for in this, so look through and mark in pencil anything you're unsure of. Practise these bits thoroughly before putting the whole piece together.

Lava

Words & Music by James Ford Murphy

Lava is a short animated film which was featured at the start of Disney/Pixar's 2015 film *Inside Out*. Written and directed by James Ford Murphy, the whole thing is a miniature musical love story, telling the tale of two volcanoes (Uku and Lele) falling in love over thousands of years. Simply sung with a ukulele accompaniment, 'Lava' was released as a single in its own right as well as being featured as a bonus song on the *Inside Out* soundtrack.

Hints & Tips: Try playing with a metronome to help you with the differing rhythms. The left hand is repetitive, so get that perfected first before fitting in the right.

Part Of Your World

Words by Howard Ashman
Music by Alan Menken

Composed by Alan Menken with lyrics by Howard Ashman, 'Part Of Your World' was one of the first songs in a Disney film that became known as the 'I want' song; a big number that shares with the audience the main character's hopes and dreams. To get more of an idea of what Ariel would be feeling, singer Jodi Benson requested that the studio's lights be dimmed to make her feel like she was underwater.

Hints & Tips: Make the whole song as expressive as you can, using the dynamics and tempo markings to create an emotional performance.

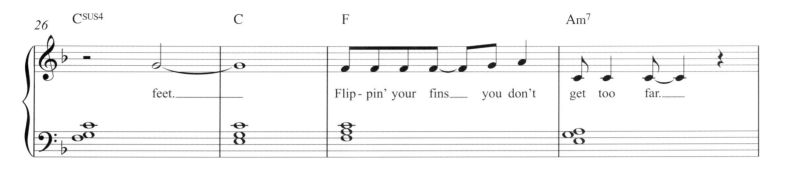

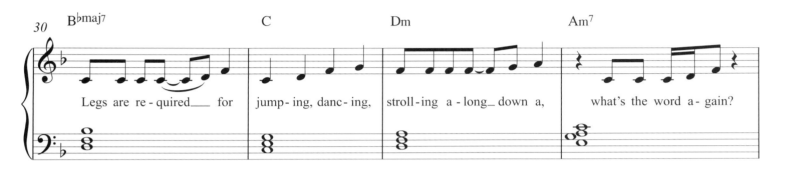

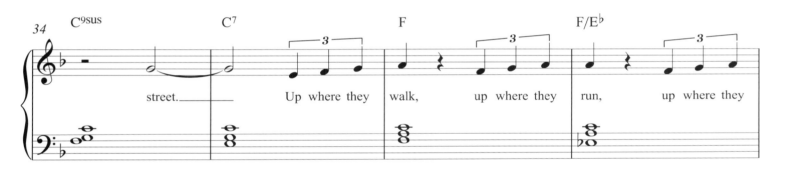

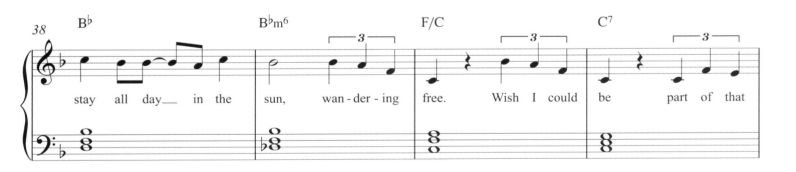

Once Upon A Dream

Words by Jack Lawrence
Music by Sammy Fain & Peter Tchaikovsky

The original 'Once Upon A Dream' was featured in 1959's *Sleeping Beauty* and was based on a waltz from Tchaikovsky's ballet of the same name. Disney re-imagined this classic story in *Maleficent* and used a sombre, slow and altogether darker cover of this song by Lana Del Rey. This version was much moodier and complemented the tone of the film brilliantly, helped by the unique vocal style of Del Rey, who was specially selected by lead actress Angelina Jolie.

Hints & Tips: Play this slowly with a haunted, dreamy feel; both hands should flow smoothly and evenly, and not plod along.

Reflection

Words by David Zippel
Music by Matthew Wilder

The 1998 film *Mulan* featured a performance of 'Reflection' by actress Lea Salonga. It was also recorded by Christina Aguilera for the single version, becoming her debut single and propelling her to pop success. Aguilera was told she had to hit a specific note to be able to sing the song, so she reportedly practised a Whitney Houston number for hours before hitting the note and getting the chance to sing the song.

Hints & Tips: While this starts in A major, there's a key change early in the piece to C major; however, there are still accidentals to watch out for.

Shut Up And Drive

**Words & Music by Peter Hook, Evan Rogers,
Carl Sturken, Bernard Sumner, Stephen Morris & Gillian Gilbert**

Used as part of the soundtrack for *Wreck-It Ralph*, Rihanna's 2007 tune has since become one of her most popular songs. Taking a sample from New Order's seminal track 'Blue Monday', Rihanna's version tends towards a heavier pop-rock feel with overdriven guitars and a 21st century beat. The song marked Rihanna's fifth top-five single in the UK, its use in the film increasing its popularity.

Hints & Tips: Wherever the right hand plays more than one note at a time, make sure you play strongly so the notes sound exactly together.

Strong

Words & Music by Patrick Doyle, Thomas Danvers & Kenneth Branagh

Composed by Patrick Doyle with Kenneth Branagh and Tommy Danvers, 'Strong' was sung by Sonna Rele for the soundtrack of the 2015 version of *Cinderella*. The song has a modern R'N'B feel that mixes contemporary drum beats with a traditionally ballad-like vocal performance from London-based singer Rele. The song builds to an uplifting ending that reflects the emotions of the character by the end of the film.

Hints & Tips: While this starts of soft and slow, it picks up in bar 25, where the rhythms get more interesting. Don't rush the first section or you'll find yourself tripping up when the rhythms get more complicated!

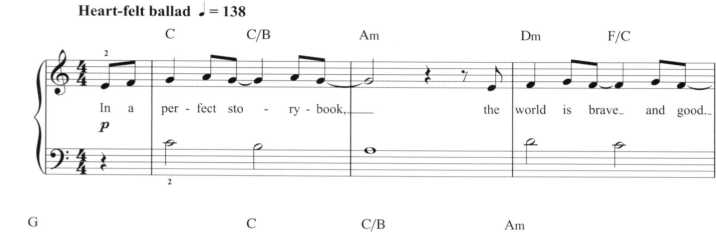

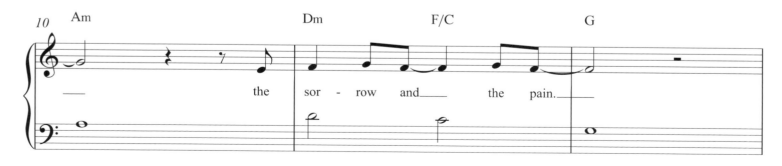

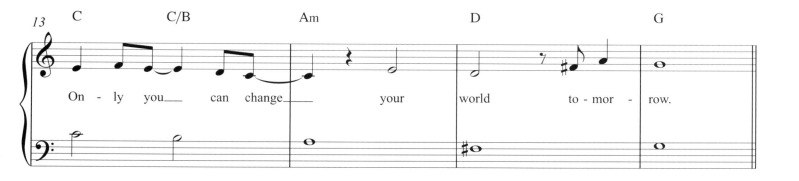

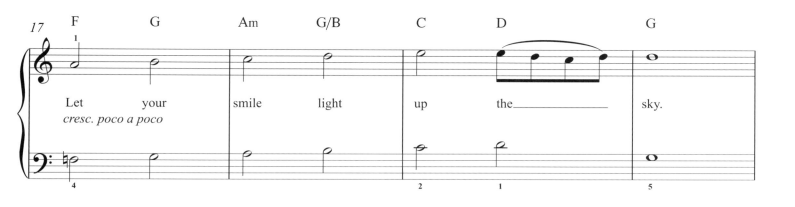

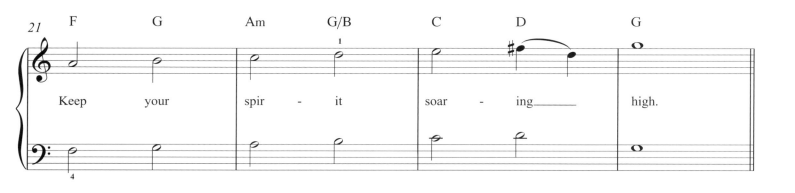

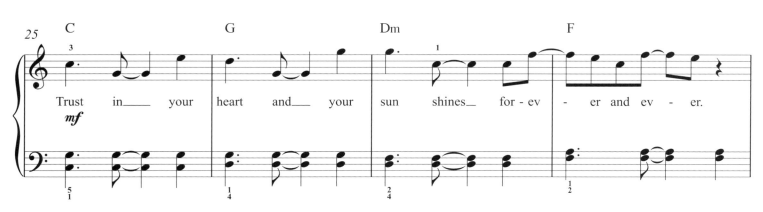

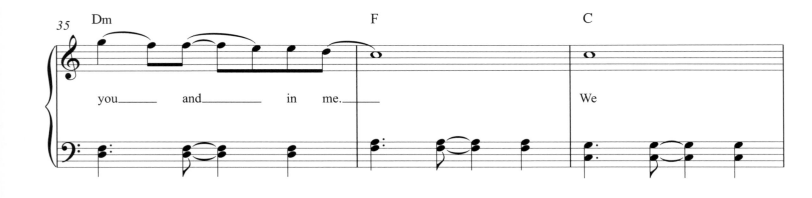

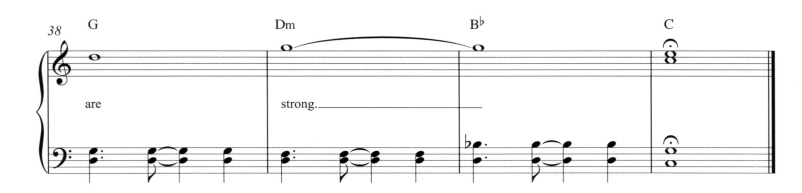

That's How You Know

Words by Stephen Schwartz
Music by Alan Menken

This song was composed for the soundtrack of *Enchanted* and, like the film, is an intentional homage to and self-parody of past famous Disney musical numbers. The music was composed by Alan Menken, who was perhaps the best man for the job considering he also composed the music for many of the older Disney films. In the film, Giselle (played by Amy Adams) sings to Robert (Patrick Dempsey) with help from a variety of people in Central Park, including buskers, dancers and a steel band.

Hints & Tips: Practise both hands separately and slowly before trying them together at the correct tempo. Make the most over the left hand wherever it has a melody that needs emphasising.

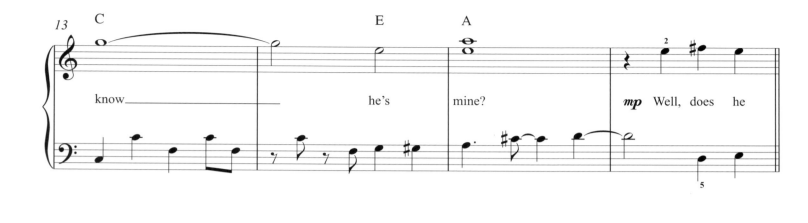

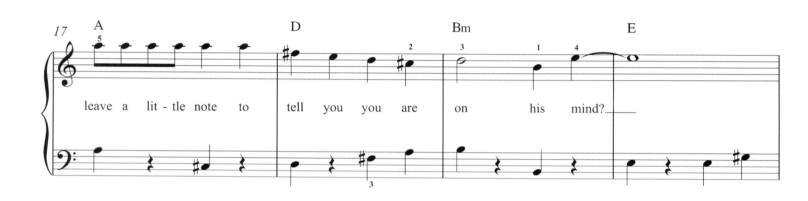

lit - tle bit ev - 'ry day._____ That's how____ you

cresc.

know. That's how____ you know he's_____ your

N.C.

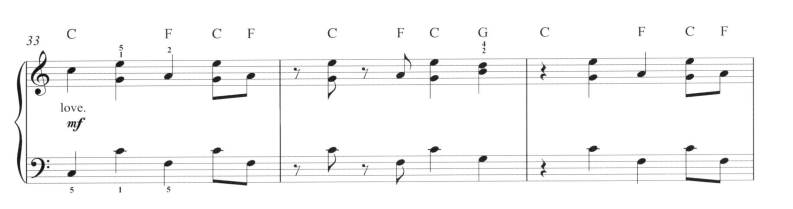

C   F   C   F   C   F   C   G   C   F   C   F

love.

mf

C   F Dm G   C   F   C   F   C   F   C   G   C

43

Touch The Sky

Words by Mark Andrews & Alexander Mandel
Music by Alexander Mandel

'Touch The Sky' is one of two original songs in *Brave* that were performed by Scottish Gaelic singer Julie Fowlis. She is known for writing and singing in the language, and the film was notable for being the first Disney film to feature it in the music. Her uplifting melody is backed by the driving rhythm of folk guitars and an array of traditional instruments, helping to enhance the Scottish Highland setting.

Hints & Tips: As this is such a fast piece, it would be a good idea to practise with a metronome, starting off slowly and building up to the correct tempo.

We Belong Together

Words & Music by Randy Newman

Randy Newman wrote this fantastically enjoyable tune for the soundtrack of *Toy Story 3*, released in 2010. Newman had previously composed music for the first two instalments of the trilogy, earning him huge acclaim from audiences and critics alike. 'We Belong Together' won the Academy Award for Best Original Song, only the singer-songwriter's second song to win the Oscar despite having received over twenty nominations.

Hints & Tips: This is rather a tricky piece so break it down into separate hands, and then into sections, and practise each bit on its own until you're really confident with it.